TOTTERING-BY-GENTLY®

TOTTERING LIFE

ANNIE TEMPEST

F

FRANCES LINCOLN LIMITED

PUBLISHERS

Photo © Garlinda Birkbeck

Frances Lincoln Limited
4 Torriano Mews
Torriano Avenue
London NW5 2RZ
www.franceslincoln.com

Tottering Life
Copyright © The O'Shea Gallery 2012
Text copyright © Annie Tempest 2012
Illustrations copyright © Annie Tempest 2012

Illustrations archived and compiled by
Raymond O'Shea

British Library Cataloguing in Publication Data
A catalogue record for this book is available from
the British Library.

ISBN 978-0-7112-3186-3
Printed in China

Bound for North Pimmshire

9 8 7 6 5 4 3 2 1

BOOKS BY ANNIE TEMPEST

2012 *Tails of Tottering Hall*
(Frances Lincoln)

2011 *She Talks Venus He Talks Mars*
(Frances Lincoln)
In the Garden with the Totterings
(Frances Lincoln)

2010 *Drinks with the Totterings*
(Frances Lincoln)
Tottering-by-Gently Annual
(Frances Lincoln)
Out & About with the Totterings
(Frances Lincoln)

2007 *At Home with the Totterings*
(The O'Shea Gallery)

2003 *Tottering-by-Gently Vol III*
(The O'Shea Gallery)

2002 *Lady Tottering's Journal*
(Orion in association with The O'Shea Gallery)

2001 *Tottering Hall*
(Orion in association with The O'Shea Gallery)

1998 *Tottering-by-Gently* (paperback)
(The O'Shea Gallery)

1998 *Tottering-by-Gently Vol II*
(The O'Shea Gallery)

1996 *Tottering-by-Gently Vol I*
(Country Life Books)

1988 *Westenders*
(Muller)

1987 *Henry on Hols*
(Muller)

1986 *Hooray Henry!*
(Muller)

1985 *How Green Are Your Wellies?*
(Muller, Blond & White)

1985 *Turbocharge Your Granny*
(Muller, Blond & White)

BOOKS ILLUSTRATED/CONTRIBUTED TO BY ANNIE TEMPEST

2002 *Why the Reindeer has a Velvet Nose* by Robin Page
(Bird's Farm Books)

2000 *The Guest from Hell* by Alistair Sampson
(Orion in association with The O'Shea Gallery)

1999 *Will I See You in Heaven?* By Michael Seed
(Blake Publishing)

1998 *Berry's Best Cellar Secrets* by Jonathan Ray
(Berry Bros. & Rudd)

1992 *Where Did I Go Wrong?* by R. Rushbrooke
(St. Paul's Publications)

1992 *Crime-check!*
(ABI)

1991 *I Will See You in Heaven Where Animals Don't Bite* by Michael Seed
(St. Paul's Publications)

1991 *Best Behaviour* by Mary Killen
(Random Century)

1989 *The Recycled Joke Book* by Anneka Rice
(Mentorn Enterprises)

1988 *Best Cartoons of the Year*
(Robson Books)

1988 *Publish and Be Damned!* by International PEN
(Heinemann Kingswood)

Instantly recognisable, Tottering-By-Gently is a jolly mirror on all our lives. Its no-nonsense philosophy has made it so much more than a cartoon strip. It is a way of life, both for the characters in it and the readers of *Country Life*. Every week, it is the turn-to page in the magazine, each of us wondering what travails or mishaps Dicky and Daffy and their entourage have got up to.

Whether gardening or partying, dieting or drinking, the pair's charm, tolerance and good humour is an unmissable pleasure. Why is it so popular and why does it work so well? I believe it is because we are laughing at ourselves through the eyes of Annie Tempest. We all aspire to live full-time in her magical world. How she does it every week is remarkable and something to be treasured. Annie's powers of observation and skill in drawing are quite exceptional.

Together with the *Spectator* column, written by Carla Carlisle, it forms one of the most successful pages in publishing history. I count myself a very lucky editor to have been bequeathed these heirlooms when I took over the chair in 2006.

Annie, thank you for making us feel better.

Mark Hedges
Editor of *Country Life*

THE TOTTERING PORTRAIT GALLERY

Lord Tottering 'Dicky'

Serena

Lady Tottering 'Daffy'

Freddy

Daisy

Gladys Shagpile

Scribble

Slobber

HonJon

TOTTERING-BY-GENTLY ®
ANNIE TEMPEST

Annie Tempest is one of the top cartoonists working in the UK. This was recognized in 2009 with the Cartoon Trust awarding her the Pont Prize for her portrayal of the British Character. Annie's cartoon career began in 1985 with the success of her first book, *How Green Are Your Wellies?* This led to a regular cartoon, 'Westenders' in the *Daily Express*. Soon after, she joined the *Daily Mail* with 'The Yuppies' cartoon strip which ran for more than seven years and for which, in 1989, she was awarded 'Strip Cartoonist of the Year'. Since 1993 Annie Tempest has been charting the life of Daffy and Dicky Tottering in Tottering-by-Gently – the phenomenally successful weekly strip cartoon in *Country Life*.

Daffy Tottering is a woman of a certain age who has been taken into the hearts of people all over the world. She reflects the problems facing women in their everyday life and is completely at one with herself, while reflecting on the intergenerational tensions and the differing perspectives of men and women, as well as dieting, ageing, gardening, fashion, food, field sports, convention and much more.

Daffy and her husband Dicky live in the fading grandeur of Tottering Hall, their stately home in the fictional country of North Pimmshire, with their extended family: daughter Serena, and grandchildren, Freddy and Daisy. The daily, Mrs Shagpile, and love of Dicky's life, Slobber, his black Labrador, and the latest addition to the family, Scribble, Daisy's working Cocker Spaniel, also make regular appearances.

Annie Tempest was born in Zambia in 1959. She has a huge international following and has had eighteen one-woman shows, from Mexico to Mayfair. Her work is now syndicated from New York to Dubai and she has had eleven collections of her cartoons published. This latest book, *Tottering Life,* is the latest volume of the 'Biennial Collection' of all the *Country Life* cartoons to be published in chronological order. This book covers the period January 2006 to December 2007.

THE O'SHEA GALLERY

Raymond O'Shea of The O'Shea Gallery was originally one of London's leading antiquarian print and map dealers. Historically, antiquarian galleries sponsored and promoted contemporary artists who they felt complemented their recognized areas of specialization. It was in this tradition that O'Shea first contacted *Country Life* magazine to see if Annie Tempest would like to be represented and sponsored by his gallery. In 1995 Raymond was appointed agent for Annie Tempest's originals and publisher of her books. Raymond is responsible for creating an archive of all of Annie's cartoons.

In 2003, the antiquarian side of his business was put on hold and the St. James's Street premises were finally converted to The Tottering Drawing Room at The O'Shea Gallery. It is now the flagship of a worldwide operation that syndicates and licenses illustrated books, prints, stationery, champagne, jigsaws, greetings cards, ties and much more. It has even launched its own fashion range of tweeds and shooting accessories under the label Gently Ltd.

The Tottering Drawing Room at The O'Shea Gallery is a wonderful location which is now available for corporate events of 45–125 people and is regularly used for private dinner parties catering for up to 14 people. Adjacent to St. James's Palace, the gallery lies between two famous 18th century shops: Berry Bros. & Rudd, the wine merchants and Locks, the hatters. Accessed through French doors at the rear of the gallery lies Pickering Place – not only the smallest public square in Great Britain, with original gas lighting, but it was also where the last duel in England was fought. A plaque on the wall, erected by the Anglo-Texan Society, indicates that from 1842–45 a building here was occupied by the Legation from the Republic of Texas to the Court of St. James.

Raymond O'Shea and Annie Tempest are delighted to be able to extend Tottering fans a warm welcome in the heart of historic St. James's where all the original Tottering watercolours can be seen along side a full product and print range.

February 23rd, 2006

He says he 'enjoys' sitting inside on this beautiful spring day, blowing people up in virtual reality...

Well, it can't be 'enjoyment' as our generation understand it...

...perhaps it's 'virtual enjoyment'...

March 30th, 2006

April 13th, 2006

April 27th, 2006

When it's good to be the third person in a marriage...

June 1st, 2006

July 6th, 2006

August 17th, 2006

August 31st, 2006

THE FEMALE CHARACTER: The prudence to reach for a chair and a drink before answering the telephone...

October 12th, 2006

October 19th, 2006

Nearly finished, Dicky! This should be the last cut of the year...

I doubt it. You've just gone over the entire lawn without the blades on...

Finally I get to sit down! It's been one of those days. How's the pheasant casserole?..

mmm...well...it certainly melts in your mouth...

...perhaps we should finish defrosting it...

My new year's resolution is to finish all the things I've started and never finished...

Now. Where did I put that box of photographs I'd started sorting into years...

Ooh! Look! Half a bottle of Baileys... I'd better start by finishing this...

Dicky and I went to drinks at the Taupe-Callico's last night...

They've redecorated the whole place in creams and whites - I hardly dared to sit on the sofa...

...and when I did I felt like a rogue scatter cushion in an accent colour...

THE GUN'S NIGHTMARE...

March 15th, 2007

THE FEMALE CHARACTER: An intuition that her guess is more accurate than her husband's certainty...

The dogs wouldn't go through the bins - it was definitely a scavenging fox...

THE GENERATION GAP: Furniture...The bean bag

It amazes me the lengths to which a man will go to avoid going outside to fetch a ladder...

July 26th, 2007

How on earth do people without horse boxes cope with trips to the bottle bank?..

August 9th, 2007

October 18th, 2007

Panel 1: Isn't that a lovely bronze, Dicky!

NORTH PIMMSHIRE ANTIQUES FAIR

Panel 2: It's by Jean-Paul Aubé - Wouldn't it look nice in the conservatory - it's very reasonable look! Only one thousand eight hundred and eighty five pounds...

TH PIMMSHIRE IQUES FAIR

Panel 3: Don't be ridiculous, Daffy! That's its date - 1885 ...

H PIMMSHIRE IQUES FAIR

BRONZE SCULPTURE JP AUBÉ

For the sake of the dogs, the British prefer not to raise their voices in anger...

November 15th, 2007

CLOSING DOWN THE GARDEN FOR WINTER...

There's always something stinging you, pricking you or getting stuck to you...

November 29th, 2007

And Granny Tottering says she would like you to repoint the chimney on your way down...

TOTTERING BRAND

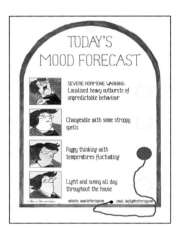

Cartoonist **Annie Tempest's** famous world of **Tottering-by-Gently**, which appears weekly in *Country Life* magazine, has spawned a wonderful range of original and stylish gifts. Her main characters, Daffy and Dicky and their extended family living at the crumbling stately pile, Tottering Hall, provide the essence for her wickedly observant humour covering all aspects of the human condition.

The Tottering range of gifts is suitable for everyone with a sense of fun. Gifts include: a large range of Signed Numbered Edition Prints, as well as digital prints On Demand (any Annie Tempest image produced as a print), books, diaries, greeting cards, postcards, tablemats, coasters, trays, noteblocks, mugs, tins, tea towels, hob covers and much more – we even have our own brand of Tottering-by-Gently Champagne . . .

You can order from our secure website at www.tottering.com or pop into our London shop: The Tottering Drawing Room at The O'Shea Gallery, at No.4, St. James's Street, SW1A 1EF, where all original artwork is available to buy.

www.tottering.com

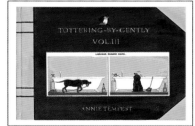

GALLERY OF SELECTED TOTTERING DESIGNS

The last leaf of Autumn...

"I'll beg and wag my tail - you try to look cute..."

'Silence at all times' is proving a little taxing for some of our senior members...

iPod...   iPad...   iPhone...   iSolation...

Santa (and his subordinate) Claus...

HAPPY CHRISTMAS

"Hello! Yup... I'm already at your Club. Don't panic - I'm wearing a suit and I'm in the library..."

Enjoying an ordinary Claret...

Pour it   Swig it
Pour it   Swig it
Pour it   Swig it
Pour it   Swig it

LIFE ISN'T ABOUT WAITING FOR THE STORM TO PASS...   ...IT'S ABOUT LEARNING TO DANCE IN THE RAIN...

It's amazing how big birthdays bring on odd behaviour in men - Dicky suddenly decided he needed a BlackBerry...   Then he decided to buy a 'top of the range' charger for it...   ...this is what he came back with...

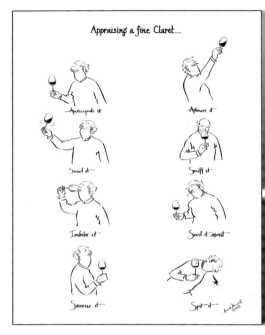

Appraising a fine Claret...

Anticipate it   Admire it
Swirl it   Sniff it
Imbibe it   Swill it about
Savour it   Spit it

Just get me a LARGE glass of wine and nobody gets hurt...

FOR IDENTIFICATION PURPOSES

MOTHER   CASH DISPENSER

Sailing is like being a toddler again - all wide eyes, big grins and permanently soggy bottoms...

THE HOSTESS
After the party...

THE HOSTESS
Before the party...

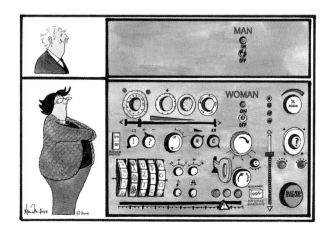

TOTTERING SELECTED PRODUCT DESIGNS